PERSEPOLIS: THE STORY OF A CHILDHOOD

by
Marjane Satrapi

Student Packet

Written by
James H Duncan

Contains masters for:

2	Prereading Activities
5	Vocabulary Activities
1	Study Guide
4	Character Analysis Activities
3	Literary Analysis Activities
2	Comprehension Activities
5	Quizzes
1	Final Test

PLUS Detailed Answer Key
and Scoring Rubric

Teacher Note

Selected activities, quizzes, and test questions in this Novel Units® Student Packet are labeled with the appropriate reading/language arts skills for quick reference. These skills can be found above quiz/test questions or sections and in the activity headings.

Note

The 2004 Pantheon paperback edition of the book, English translation © 2003 by L'Association, Paris, France, was used to prepare this guide. The page references may differ in other editions. Book ISBN: 0-375-71457-X

Please note: This book deals with sensitive, mature issues. Parts may contain profanity, sexual references, and/or descriptions of violence. Please assess the appropriateness of this book for the age level and maturity of your students prior to reading and discussing it with them.

To order, contact your local school supply store, or—
Novel Units, Inc.
P.O. Box 97
Bulverde, TX 78163-0097

Web site: novelunits.com

Note to the Teacher

Selected activities, quizzes, and test questions in this Novel Units® Student Packet are labeled with the following reading/language arts skills for quick reference. These skills can be found above quiz/test questions or sections and in the activity headings.

Basic Understanding: The student will demonstrate a basic understanding of written texts. The student will:
- use a text's structure or other sources to locate and recall information (Locate Information)
- determine main idea and identify relevant facts and details (Main Idea and Details)
- use prior knowledge and experience to comprehend and bring meaning to a text (Prior Knowledge)
- summarize major ideas in a text (Summarize Major Ideas)

Literary Elements: The student will apply knowledge of literary elements to understand written texts. The student will:
- analyze characters from a story (Character Analysis)
- analyze conflict and problem resolution (Conflict/Resolution)
- recognize and interpret literary devices (flashback, foreshadowing, symbolism, simile, metaphor, etc.) (Literary Devices)
- consider characters' points of view (Point of View)
- recognize and analyze a story's setting (Setting)
- understand and explain themes in a text (Theme)

Analyze Written Texts: The student will use a variety of strategies to analyze written texts. The student will:
- identify the author's purpose (Author's Purpose)
- identify cause and effect relationships in a text (Cause/Effect)
- identify characteristics representative of a given genre (Genre)
- interpret information given in a text (Interpret Text)
- make and verify predictions with information from a text (Predictions)
- sequence events in chronological order (Sequencing)
- identify and use multiple text formats (Text Format)
- follow written directions and write directions for others to follow (Follow/Write Directions)

Critical Thinking: The student will apply critical-thinking skills to analyze written texts. The student will:
- write and complete analogies (Analogies)
- find similarities and differences throughout a text (Compare/Contrast)
- draw conclusions from information given (Drawing Conclusions)
- make and explain inferences (Inferences)
- respond to texts by making connections and observations (Making Connections)
- recognize and identify the mood of a text (Mood)
- recognize an author's style and how it affects a text (Style)
- support responses by referring to relevant aspects of a text (Support Responses)
- recognize and identify the author's tone (Tone)
- write to entertain, such as through humorous poetry or short stories (Write to Entertain)
- write to express ideas (Write to Express)
- write to inform (Write to Inform)
- write to persuade (Write to Persuade)
- demonstrate understanding by creating visual images based on text descriptions (Visualizing)
- practice math skills as they relate to a text (Math Skills)

Getting the "Lay of the Land"

Directions: Prepare for reading by answering the following short-answer questions.

1. Who is the author?

   _____

2. What does the title suggest to you about the book?

   _____

   _____

   _____

   _____

3. When was the book first copyrighted?

   _____

4. How many pages are there in the book?

   _____

5. Thumb through the book. Read three pages—one from near the beginning, one from near the middle, and one from near the end. What predictions can you make about the book?

   _____

   _____

   _____

   _____

   _____

6. What does the cover suggest to you about the book?

   _____

   _____

   _____

   _____

Name _____

Anticipation Guide

Directions: Rate each of the following statements before you read the book, and discuss your ratings with a partner. After you have completed the book, rate and discuss the statements again.

1 —————— 2 —————— 3 —————— 4 —————— 5 —————— 6
strongly agree   strongly disagree

	Before	**After**
1. You should never leave your family behind in times of trouble.	_____	_____
2. People who spend long periods of time in prison are not good role models.	_____	_____
3. It is okay to believe everything the government tells you.	_____	_____
4. During times of war, people often act on emotions rather than facts.	_____	_____
5. Social status has no effect on relationships.	_____	_____
6. "To die a martyr is to inject blood into the veins of society."	_____	_____
7. Receiving a good education is worth risking your life.	_____	_____
8. Children should be able to fight in wars if they believe in the cause.	_____	_____
9. Governments should not be allowed to control what students learn in school.	_____	_____
10. Lying to your neighbors is okay if it improves their opinion of you.	_____	_____

© Novel Units, Inc.

Name _____

Vocabulary Synonyms

obligatory	decadence	avant-garde	imperialism
degenerate	putsch	entourage	rheumatism
splendor	frivolities		

Directions: Choose the word or phrase closest in meaning to the vocabulary word as it is used in the book. Then use at least four of the words in a brief analysis of Marjane's childhood.

_____ 1. **obligatory:** (a) rented   (b) redeemed   (c) required   (d) rejected

_____ 2. **decadence:** (a) corruption (b) coincidence (c) confidence (d) confusion

_____ 3. **avant-garde:** (a) fiery   (b) futuristic   (c) false   (d) familiar

_____ 4. **imperialism:** (a) declaration (b) domesticism (c) depreciation (d) domination

_____ 5. **degenerate:** (a) waste   (b) worsen   (c) welcome   (d) widen

_____ 6. **putsch:**   (a) ridge   (b) revolt   (c) revenge   (d) rumor

_____ 7. **entourage:** (a) fighters   (b) fireworks   (c) fortifications (d) followers

_____ 8. **rheumatism:** (a) sterility   (b) stiffness   (c) silence   (d) servitude

_____ 9. **splendor:**   (a) bravery   (b) briefness   (c) brilliance   (d) bewilderment

_____ 10. **frivolities:** (a) nonsense   (b) nervousness   (c) nicknames   (d) negotiations

Name _____

Word Map

clandestine	jackals	effigy	phenomena
euphoria	subversive	conviction	irretrievable
diabolical	exile		

Directions: Complete the word map below for six of the vocabulary words above.

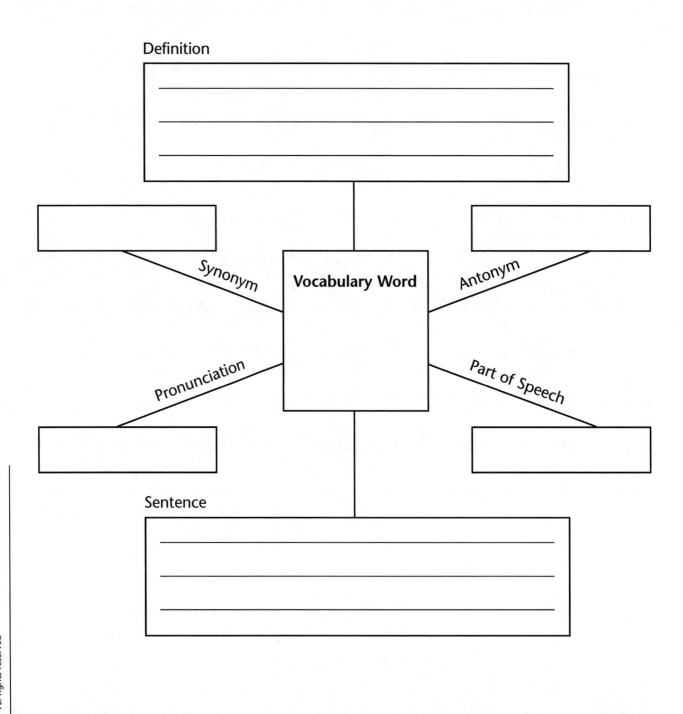

Definition

Synonym **Vocabulary Word** Antonym

Pronunciation Part of Speech

Sentence

Vocabulary Sentence Sets

transitional	divine	proletariat	fundamentalist
progressive	pretext	defeatist	console
intolerable			

Directions: Write the vocabulary words from the list above on the numbered lines below.

1. _____ 2. _____

3. _____ 4. _____

5. _____ 6. _____

7. _____ 8. _____

9. _____

On a separate sheet of paper, use each of the following sets of words in an original sentence. Your sentences should show that you know the meanings of the vocabulary words as they are used in the story.

Sentence 1: words 8 and 3
Sentence 2: words 9 and 5
Sentence 3: words 4 and 2
Sentence 4: words 1 and 7
Sentence 5: words 5 and 2
Sentence 6: words 6 and 3
Sentence 7: words 2 and 1
Sentence 8: words 6 and 4
Sentence 9: words 7 and 9
Sentence 10: words 5 and 8

Newspaper

reservoir	resignation	carnage	denounce
bearable	vintner	maternal	ideology
repression	belligerent	asylum	

Directions: Imagine you are a journalist writing a news story about an event that happens in this section. Use the vocabulary words above in your investigative news story. You may use more paper if necessary.

Tehran Times

Wednesday, October 2 • Section A, Page 1

_____

_____

_____

_____

_____

_____

_____

_____

_____

_____

_____

_____

_____

_____

Name _____

Synonym or Antonym?

occupied	permissive	ballistic	confirmation
fatalism	circumspect	aggressor	bureaucrats
dowry			

Directions: Each sentence below contains an antonym or synonym of a vocabulary word in the box above. Write the correct related vocabulary word in the provided space, and circle all antonyms.

1. The airborne baseball smashed the window, and the children ran in terror.

   _____

2. The bride's parents shipped the impressive wedding gift all the way from France.

   _____

3. Robert's resigned acceptance of his impossible situation disappointed his family.

   _____

4. The new teacher's strict rules made life difficult for the students.

   _____

5. The people held a parade when the revolution liberated the city.

   _____

6. The visiting officials stood behind the mayor as she gave a speech.

   _____

7. The witnesses only provided hearsay evidence during the trial.

   _____

8. Lena had a difficult time writing her report about the novel's antagonist.

   _____

9. The soldiers were nervous about their captain's reckless behavior.

   _____

Name _____

Directions: On a separate sheet of paper, write a brief answer to each question as you read the book at home or in class. Use the questions to guide your reading, prepare for class discussions, and review for quizzes and tests.

The Veil–Persepolis

1. How do the students react to having to wear a veil? Why do they act this way?

2. Why does Marjane want to be a prophet? What does she write in her book?

3. What kind of relationship does Marjane have with God, and what do they discuss? What happens to this relationship over time?

4. What has Iran experienced over the last 2,500 years?

5. What happens at the Rex Cinema? Who is to blame for the incident?

6. How did Reza come into power? What ulterior motive did people have for helping Reza?

7. Why did Marjane's grandfather decide to become a Communist?

8. Review pages 27 through 29 of the book, and discuss how the Shah runs the country. Why do you think people are upset with his methods?

9. What is ironic about the "martyr" at the hospital?

10. What image in this section stands out the most to you, and why? What special meaning do you think it holds?

The Letter–Moscow

1. Who is Marjane's favorite author? What kind of stories does he tell? How do they make Marjane feel?

2. What kind of relationship does Marjane have with Mehri? Explain.

3. Whom does Mehri fall in love with, and how do they communicate? Why does the relationship fail?

4. What concessions does the Shah make to the protestors, and what is the end result?

5. How does Marjane's father feel after the Shah's departure?

6. What changes does Marjane notice in her neighbors? Why do you think they change?

7. Why were Siamak and Mohsen in prison, and what happened to them there?

8. In what way does the artist show Marjane's shame on page 52 of the book?

9. Why does Anoosh leave Iran, where does he go, and what happens to him there?

10. Why does Anoosh return to Iran, and what happens when he arrives?

11. What image in this section stands out the most to you, and why? What special meaning do you think it holds?

The Sheep–The Jewels

1. Why is Marjane upset by her father's comments?

2. How do the Satrapis react when many of their family and friends leave Iran?

3. Why does Siamak flee the country with his family?

4. What do Marjane and Anoosh discuss in their final conversation?

5. What reason does the government give for closing the universities?

6. Discuss what is happening on page 77 of the book, and explain the artistic choices that make the details of this image clear and understandable.

7. How do Marjane and her father react to the news about the bombing of Iraq? What suddenly changes these feelings?

8. Describe the two essays that are read in Marjane's class and the effect each has on the teacher.

9. Who comes to stay with the Satrapis, and how are they different from the Satrapis?

10. Why do Mali and Taji feel humiliated in the store?

11. What image in this section stands out the most to you, and why? What special meaning do you think it holds?

The Key–The Passport

1. Describe the Persian "philosophy of resignation." Who in Marjane's family embodies this philosophy?

2. What kinds of religious rituals do the students perform in school? What kinds of similar rituals had the students seen before?

3. How do the students rebel against the rituals, and how do their parents react?

4. According to the Iranian government, what will the keys do for the children? In reality, what are the keys?

5. What illegal activities do the Satrapis participate in, and how do they hide these activities?

6. Why do the soldiers follow Marjane's family home, and how do the Satrapis get out of trouble?

7. What does Iraq offer to Iran, and how does Iran react?

Name _____

8. Where does Marjane go to think? What does she do there, and why is it significant?

9. What does Marjane see when she first arrives at the hospital? What do these people have in common?

10. Why is Eby unable to acquire a passport, and what happens before the real passport arrives?

11. What image in this section stands out the most to you, and why? What special meaning do you think it holds?

Kim Wilde–The Dowry

1. Where do Marjane's parents go for vacation, and what gifts does Marjane ask them to bring back?

2. How are Marjane's parents able to sneak the posters into Iran, and what other gifts do they bring Marjane?

3. Why is Marjane stopped and harassed in the street? How does she get out of this situation?

4. What new threat terrorizes Tehran, and why do the Satrapis stay?

5. Why does Marjane run home, and what does she see there? How does she know that her friend is dead?

6. Why does Marjane get in trouble with the principal, and how does Marjane react to the principal's accusations?

7. How is Marjane able to find a new school, and what happens once she is there?

8. Why do Marjane's parents believe that sending her to Austria is a good idea?

9. What is Marjane's grandmother's parting advice?

10. What is the last thing Marjane sees before she leaves for Europe?

11. What image in this section stands out the most to you, and why? What special meaning do you think it holds?

Name _____

Persepolis: The Story of a Childhood
Activity #8 • Character Analysis
Use During and After Reading
(*Character Analysis/Sequencing*)

Feelings

Directions: Complete the chart below to analyze Marjane's feelings in *Persepolis.*

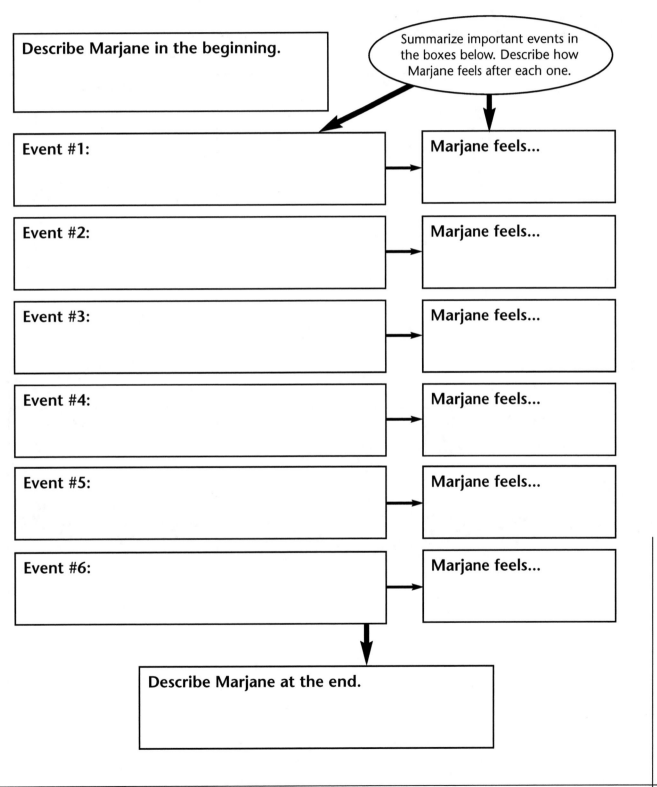

Describe Marjane in the beginning.

Summarize important events in the boxes below. Describe how Marjane feels after each one.

Event #1:

Marjane feels...

Event #2:

Marjane feels...

Event #3:

Marjane feels...

Event #4:

Marjane feels...

Event #5:

Marjane feels...

Event #6:

Marjane feels...

Describe Marjane at the end.

Name _____

Sorting Characters

Directions: Similarities between characters are sometimes a clue to themes in a story. Place this book's characters in one or more of the groups below. Then choose one group of characters from the chart, and write a paragraph on a separate sheet of paper explaining how they represent a theme in *Persepolis.*

Victims	Victimizers	Fighters
Peace-lovers	**Conformists**	**Self-directors**

Name _____

Persepolis: The Story of a Childhood
Activity #10 • Character Analysis
Use During and After Reading
(Character Analysis)

Bio-poem

Directions: Using the format below, write a bio-poem about the protagonist. Then write a bio-poem about yourself using the same format. Write a paragraph describing the values and characteristics you share.

—Line 1: First name only
—Line 2: Lover of (list three things the character loves)
—Line 3: Giver of (list three things the character gives)
—Line 4: Needs (list three things the character needs)
—Line 5: Wants (list three things the character wants)
—Line 6: Is good at (list three things the character is good at)
—Line 7: Should work on (list three things the character needs to improve)
—Line 8: Is similar to (list three other characters to whom this character is similar and list a reason behind each character)
—Line 9: Survivor of (list three things the character survives)
—Line 10: Last name only

Title _____

1. _____
2. _____
3. _____
4. _____
5. _____
6. _____
7. _____
8. _____
9. _____
10. _____

Name _____

Persepolis: The Story of a Childhood
Activity #11 • Literary Analysis
Use During and After Reading
(Literary Devices)

Foreshadowing Chart

Foreshadowing is the literary technique of giving clues to coming events in a story.

Directions: What examples of foreshadowing do you recall from the story? If necessary, skim through the chapters to find examples of foreshadowing. List at least four examples below. Explain what clues are given, and then list the coming event that is suggested.

Foreshadowing	Page #	Clues	Coming Event

Effects of Reading

Directions: When reading a graphic novel, each image of the book may affect you in a different way. Think about how images in *Persepolis* affected you in different ways. Did some parts make you laugh? cry? want to do something to help someone? Below, redraw images from the book that touched each of the following parts of the body: your head (made you think), your heart (made you feel), your funny bone (made you laugh), or your feet (spurred you to action).

Your head	**Your heart**
Your funny bone	**Your feet**

Name _____

Time Line

Directions: In the diagram below, write about four sequential events the author includes in the book that challenge or enhance Marjane's beliefs. In the numbered boxes, explain each event, and in the larger boxes, explain how the event challenges and/or changes Marjane's ideas on faith or politics.

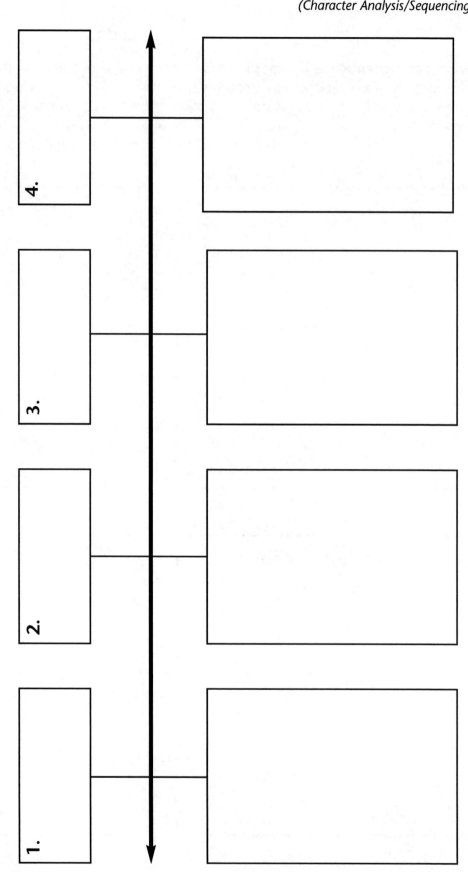

Name _____

Using Dialogue

Directions: Choose some dialogue from the book. Fill in the chart to evaluate the purpose of the dialogue and whether or not it is effective in moving along the plot.

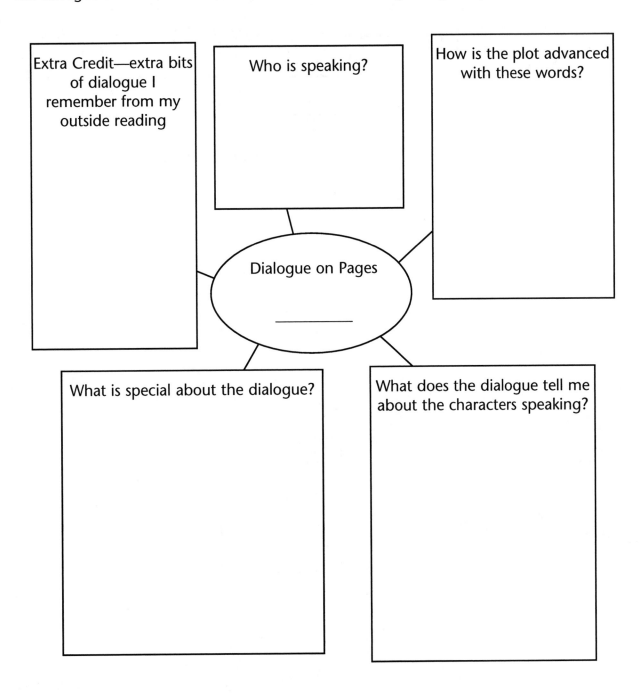

Extra Credit—extra bits of dialogue I remember from my outside reading

Who is speaking?

How is the plot advanced with these words?

Dialogue on Pages
_____

What is special about the dialogue?

What does the dialogue tell me about the characters speaking?

Name _____

Story Map

Directions: Complete the story map below.

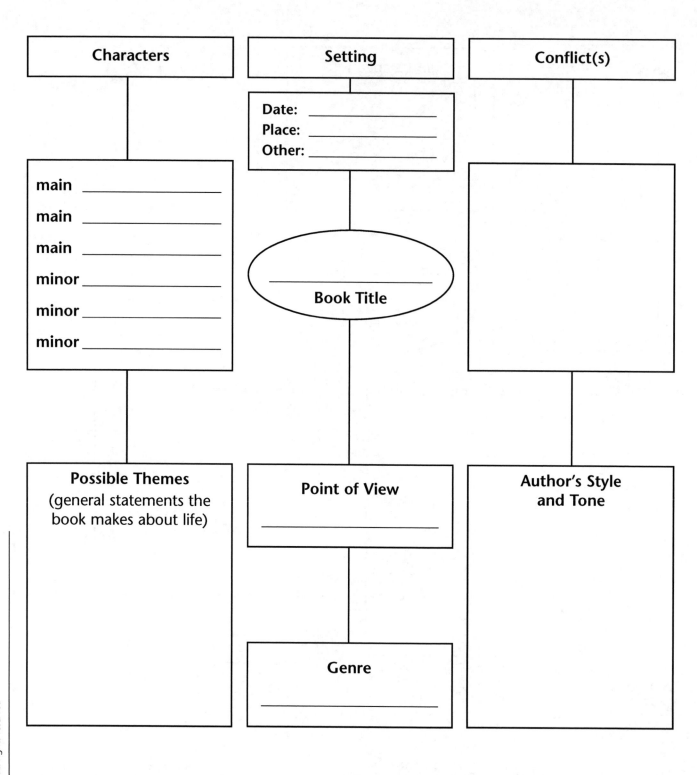

Name _____

Themes and Symbols

Directions: List major themes from the book in the left column. In the center column, list symbols or images that you find throughout the book representing that theme. In the right column, explain briefly how those symbols relate to the theme.

Theme	Symbol/Image	Relationship

Name _____

Name _____

(Main Idea and Details)

A. True/False: Mark each with a *T* for true or an *F* for false.

____ 1. Marjane wants to be a politician or author when she grows up.

____ 2. In exchange for oil, Reza is offered the position of emperor.

____ 3. Marjane likes to imagine herself as Fidel Castro.

____ 4. Marjane's mother must change her appearance after being photographed demonstrating.

____ 5. Influential Russians offer to help Reza overthrow the Iranian government.

(Main Idea and Details)

B. Fill in the Blanks

6. The mob at the hospital wants to glorify the old woman's husband as a(n)

_____.

7. Marjane tells her parents that she wants to be a(n) _____ but tells

God that she wants to be a(n) _____.

8. Marjane says, "The _____ is like a _____.
When the wheels don't turn, it falls."

9. Marjane's _____ was put into a cell which was filled with

_____ for hours at a time.

10. _____ wants to make Iran "the most modern [nation] of all time."

(Style/Support Responses)

C. Open-Ended Comprehension: On the lines below, explain at least one artistic choice the author makes in this section that enhances your understanding of the book.

_____

_____

_____

_____

_____

_____

_____

© Novel Units, Inc.

Name _____

(Summarize Major Ideas)
A. Short Answer: Write brief answers to the following questions.

1. What kind of stories does Marjane's favorite author write?

    _____

2. Why doesn't Marjane's father believe that peace will come to Iran in the near future?

    _____

3. According to Marjane, what does it take to be a hero?

    _____

4. Why did Siamak and Mohsen spend time in prison?

    _____

5. What kind of relationship do Marjane and Mehri share?

    _____

(Main Idea and Details)
B. True/False: Mark each with a *T* for true or an *F* for false.

_____ 6. Marjane's mother teaches Mehri to read and write love letters.

_____ 7. Marjane's father tells stories of how he was tortured in prison.

_____ 8. Uncle Anoosh was exiled from Iran for teaching Communism.

_____ 9. Marjane likes to brag about the members of her family who spent time in prison.

_____ 10. The neighbor refuses to date Mehri because she is a maid.

(Character Analysis/Point of View)
C. Open-Ended Comprehension: On the lines below, explain in detail why Marjane respects Uncle Anoosh so much.

_____

_____

_____

_____

_____

Name _____

(Main Idea and Details)
A. Fill in the Blanks

1. Anoosh calls _____ the "_____ of [his] life" before

    he is executed for being a "Russian _____."

2. The government closes the _____ for two years because they are

    _____.

3. Marjane reveals that there are now two kinds of women: _____

    women and modern women.

4. When Marjane returns from a vacation, her _____ says that Iran has

    been attacked by _____ and there is now a war in progress.

5. Eby thinks Mali's husband is too _____.

(Character Analysis)
B. Identification: Match each character with the correct description.

_____ 6. Mali   a. is murdered by the Iranian government

_____ 7. Marjane   b. escapes to Tehran after a bombing

_____ 8. Pardisse   c. escapes the Iranian government

_____ 9. Siamak   d. cries during the national anthem

_____ 10. Mohsen   e. wrote about her dead father

(Style/Support Responses)
C. Open-Ended Comprehension: On the lines below, explain at least one artistic choice the author makes in this section that enhances your understanding of the book.

_____

_____

_____

_____

_____

_____

_____

_____

| © Novel Units, Inc.

(Summarize Major Ideas)
A. Short Answer: Write brief answers to the following questions.

1. What does the government tell the children about the key? What is it actually?

   _____

2. Why does Taji put tape and heavy curtains on the windows?

   _____

3. Why is Jordan Avenue so enticing to Marjane?

   _____

4. Why does Uncle Taher need a passport?

   _____

5. What news does Shahab give Marjane and Taji?

   _____

(Main Idea and Details)
B. True/False: Mark each with a *T* for true or an *F* for false.

____ 6. Iran's army is small but has much better weapons than Iraq.

____ 7. Uncle Taher dies before his real passport arrives.

____ 8. Marjane escapes to the roof to be alone and relax.

____ 9. Eby is arrested for trying to bribe a police officer.

____ 10. The government bans decks of cards and board games, as well as alcohol.

(Literary Devices)
C. Open-Ended Comprehension: On the lines below, explain the irony behind the phrase "imposed peace."

_____

_____

_____

_____

_____

_____

_____

(Main Idea and Details)
A. True/False: Mark each with a *T* for true or an *F* for false.

_____ 1. Marjane is hurt when her friends begin to ask for her personal belongings.

_____ 2. Marjane believes that you should always shout louder than your aggressor.

_____ 3. During the bombing, the Satrapis stay in Tehran so Eby can keep his job.

_____ 4. Marjane goes to Gandhi Avenue to buy black-market music.

_____ 5. Marjane asks her parents to bring her makeup and a leather jacket from Greece.

(Main Idea and Details)
B. Fill in the Blanks

6. Eby is able to hide the _____ inside his jacket and sneak them past the customs official when he and Taji return from a vacation in _____.

7. The Guardians of the _____ interrogate Marjane about her

_____.

8. Marjane's parents want to send her to _____ so she can continue her education.

9. A(n) _____ is a gift a husband gives the bride's family, but the _____ gives them to families as an insult.

10. Eby says Iranians love to _____ and that his natural optimism leads him to be _____.

(Style/Support Responses)
C. Open-Ended Comprehension: On the lines below, explain at least one artistic choice the author makes in this section that enhances your understanding of the book.

_____

_____

_____

_____

_____

_____

_____

© Novel Units, Inc.

Name _____

(Character Analysis)
A. Identification: Match each character with the correct description.

____ 1. Taji

____ 2. Marjane

____ 3. Anoosh

____ 4. Uncle Taher

____ 5. Shahab

____ 6. Mehri

____ 7. Eby

____ 8. Grandmother

____ 9. Mali

____ 10. Pardisse

a. misses his son greatly

b. takes photos of violent demonstrations

c. comes up with the idea to hide posters in a jacket

d. escapes to Tehran after a bombing

e. reminds Marjane that she must stay true to herself

f. reveals that children are being sent to war

g. is executed for being a "Russian spy"

h. is a victim of the Iranian class struggle

i. loses her father in the war with Iraq

j. writes love letters

B. Multiple Choice: Choose the BEST answer.

(Cause/Effect)

____ 11. Taji slaps Marjane and Mehri because they

(a) went to a party

(b) refused to wear veils

(c) attended a demonstration

(d) wrote love letters to a neighbor

(Main Idea and Details)

____ 12. British businessmen offer Reza the position of emperor in exchange for

(a) fighter jets

(b) gold

(c) land

(d) oil

(Literary Devices)

____ 13. The image of a demon curling around the Satrapis is an example of

    (a) flashback

    (b) foreshadowing

    (c) hyperbole

    (d) simile

(Main Idea and Details)

____ 14. What information does Marjane keep in her "holy book"?

    (a) her prayers

    (b) a list of rules

    (c) her complaints

    (d) a list of philosophers

(Character Analysis)

____ 15. Marjane can best be described as

    (a) principled

    (b) selfish

    (c) timid

    (d) vengeful

(Cause/Effect)

____ 16. Marjane is expelled from school because she

    (a) shoved the principal

    (b) stole someone's bracelet

    (c) spoke out about the government

    (d) attended a demonstration with her parents

(Cause/Effect)

____ 17. What causes Uncle Taher's final heart attack?

    (a) Scud missiles

    (b) a demonstration

    (c) an exploding grenade

    (d) sadness over his son's absence

(Theme)

____18. The Iranian government's use of the golden keys to attract child soldiers is an example of which theme?

(a) coming of age

(b) family solidarity

(c) religion and politics

(d) the struggle for freedom

(Main Idea and Details)

____19. Pardisse is praised for writing an essay about

(a) her father's death

(b) the ongoing class struggle

(c) the effective demonstrations

(d) Iran's long and violent history

(Main Idea and Details)

____20. Why does the government agree to play the national anthem?

(a) to rally protestors

(b) so citizens will feel patriotic

(c) to inspire soldiers to fight hard

(d) so imprisoned pilots will agree to fight the Iraqis

(Literary Devices)

____21. The phrase "star of my life" becomes darkly ironic when Marjane finds herself feeling

(a) angry

(b) distant

(c) loved

(d) relieved

(Main Idea and Details)
C. Fill in the Blanks

22. The government says it is better to have no students at all than to educate future

    _____.

23. The _____ students take over the U.S. _____,
    calling it "a nest of spies."

24. The government often gives families a(n) _____ when they execute
    young women who are virgins.

25. Uncle Anoosh gives Marjane two _____ made of

    _____ as gifts.

26. Eby says, "...as long as there is _____ in the Middle East, we will

    never have _____."

27. After Marjane turns 14, she becomes much more _____.

28. After _____ is executed, Marjane tells _____ that
    she never wants to see him again.

29. Marjane discovers that her grandfather was a(n) _____, but he

    became a(n) _____ when he saw how Reza treated the people of Iran.

D. Short Answer: In one paragraph each, answer three of the following on a separate sheet of paper.

(Literary Devices)
(a) Explain the importance of the images of Marjane holding a scale, making the peace sign, and holding a sword and shield.

(Character Analysis)
(b) How does Marjane react to learning about her grandfather's fate and torture?

(Compare/Contrast)
(c) Compare and contrast Marjane's and Eby's reactions to developments in the war.

(Literary Devices)
(d) Explain the symbolism of the juxtaposed images of child soldiers in an explosion and young people dancing.

(Author's Purpose)
(e) Explain the importance of the book's final image. Why do you think the author ended the book with this image?

E. Essay: Complete one of the following in a well-developed essay. Cite specific evidence from the book to support your answer.

(Character Analysis)
(a) Does Marjane's definition of a hero change throughout the story? Does Marjane view her parents as heroes? How do you know?

(Interpret Text/Support Responses)
(b) Do you feel that Iran's leaders are sincere in their religious beliefs, or do you think they only mean to use religion as a tool to manipulate Iran's citizens? How might the author respond to this question? Explain.

(Write to Express)
(c) How does the artwork in *Persepolis* enhance or detract from the reading experience? Is this an effective method of storytelling? Why or why not?

Answer Key

Activity #1: 1. Marjane Satrapi 2. Answers will vary. 3. 2000 4. 154 5.–6. Answers will vary.

Activity #2: Answers will vary.

Activity #3: 1. c 2. a 3. b 4. d 5. b 6. b 7. d 8. b 9. c 10. a

Activity #4: Answers will vary. Example: Word—exile; Definition—voluntary absence from one's own country; Synonym—isolation, banishment; Antonym—inclusion, welcome; Part of Speech—noun; Pronunciation—ĕg'zīl; Sentence—The president went into *exile* after the revolution.

Activity #5: Sentences will vary.

Activity #6: News stories will vary.

Activity #7: 1. ballistic/airborne 2. dowry/gift 3. fatalism/acceptance 4. permissive/strict 5. occupied/liberated 6. bureaucrats/officials 7. confirmation/hearsay 8. aggressor/antagonist 9. circumspect/reckless; antonyms— *4, 5, 7, 9*

Study Guide

The Veil–Persepolis: 1. The students make fun of the veil, play with it, and do not take it seriously; Before the revolution and the new rules, the students attended a secular French-language school, and they had a lot more freedom there. 2. Marjane wants to be a prophet because she sees many unjust things happening around her, such as her maid eating in a separate room, her family living a privileged life, and her grandmother living with pain; Marjane keeps a list of rules that she thinks will make the world a fair place in which to live. 3. They have a warm, personal relationship. They talk all the time about her desire to be a prophet. She tells God that she wants to be "justice, love and the wrath of God all in one" (p. 9); As time passes, and as Marjane educates herself about the realities of her world, she loses interest in keeping up her relationship with God. Though He tries to speak with her, even about mundane topics, she is often preoccupied. 4. Iran suffered through 2,500 years of "tyranny and submission" at the hands of their own emperors and imperialist nations. It is a history filled with violence and suffering. 5. The doors of the theater are locked, and the building is set ablaze. Police make sure no one is able to help those inside, and they attack the people outside the theater. Firemen do not arrive until 40 minutes later, and 400 people die. The Shah blames religious fanatics, but the people know he is to blame. 6. Reza started out as "an illiterate low-ranking officer" (p. 20) who wanted to start a revolution in Iran to install a republic. Western powers and "influential British" learned of his plan and offered to help his cause and guarantee him a place as dictator; They wanted control of Iran's massive oil resources. 7. After speaking to intellectuals, he saw that the class system in Iran was tearing the nation apart, and he believed this was an injustice that Communism could solve. 8. The Shah speaks of Iran's splendor and spends a fortune on lavish events, parades, and celebrations, many of which honor the great leaders of the past. Many people see through this charade and feel the Shah is bankrupting Iran to impress heads of state. 9. The man who died at the hospital was not killed by the police or the Shah. The protestors, in their hysteria, are unable to comprehend that the man died of cancer and glorify him as a martyr. When his wife tries to stop them, they tell her that he is a hero, and she joins in their march. 10. Answers will vary.

The Letter–Moscow: 1. Ali Ashraf Darvishian; He writes Charles Dickens-type stories, sad but true tales about children who must work brutal jobs just to survive; She feels guilty for living a privileged life. 2. She has a sisterly relationship with Mehri. Mehri takes care of Marjane, plays games with her, sometimes finishes her food, and tells her scary stories. 3. Mehri falls for the boy next door, and Marjane writes and reads letters for Mehri; Eby tells the boy that Mehri is actually a maid and not Marjane's sister. Because of the class difference, the boy loses all interest in Mehri. 4. He attempts to make some democratic reforms and tries to choose a Prime Minister, but he is too picky and the Iranian people have already lost all patience with him. He finally agrees to step down from power. 5. While he is glad that the Shah has left Iran, he knows that Iran will always have trouble so long as it has vast oil deposits. 6. The neighbors all begin to act as if they sacrificed and suffered for the sake of the revolution, even if they did not; Answers will vary, but the people likely want to feel like they played a part, even if they did not. They also want to show that they are part of the winning side and distance themselves from the losing side. 7. They are both regarded as Communists and political enemies of the state. Mohsen is a revolutionary, and Siamak writes subversive articles about the government. They both endured horrific torture in prison. 8. Marjane shrinks in the images at the bottom of page 52 because she feels small. Satrapi depicts herself this way to show that Laly's and Taji's comments make her feel ashamed. 9. Anoosh's uncle declared a section of Iran as a new state, and Anoosh helped his uncle run this new province, but the

Iranian government cracked down on these revolutionaries. Anoosh fled to Moscow to escape the police. He studied Communism at the university there, got married, and had children. 10. Anoosh's marriage deteriorated, and he divorced his wife. He misses his family in Iran and tries to sneak back in, but he is arrested at the border and sent to prison. 11. Answers will vary.

The Sheep–The Jewels: 1. Marjane thinks Eby is upset with her, but he is only reacting angrily to the inaccurate news. 2. Marjane is upset that her friends left for America. Her mother wonders if they are making a mistake by staying. Her father tries to assure them that staying is for the best, but his face reveals that he is also worried. 3. When Mohsen's body is discovered, people begin to worry that the government is trying to kill former political prisoners. The police go to Siamak's house and kill his sister. Siamak then flees the country in order to avoid the government's purge of political dissidents. 4. Anoosh tells Marjane that she is the daughter he always wished he had, that the proletariat will someday rule Iran, and that she is the "star of [his] life" (p. 69). 5. They say all of the books and teaching materials are "decadent" and need to be "revised." They say they would rather close the schools for a while than have their students turn into imperialists. 6. The family leaves Iran and goes on vacation to Italy and Spain for three weeks. Satrapi shows how wonderful the trip is by showing herself and her parents on a flying carpet with swirling wind and exciting sights all around them. In this picture, life outside of Iran appears idyllic and the love that unites the Satrapis as a family is clearly evident. 7. They cheer and are thrilled that the Iranian military is defending their country; When they hear that many Iranians died in the fight, they become somber. 8. Marjane's essay is about the history and warfare of Iran, and her teacher is not very interested. Pardisse writes an essay about losing her father in the current war, and the teacher is very impressed and cries. 9. Mali, Taji's childhood friend, arrives at the Satrapis' doorstep with her family after their home is destroyed in a bombing. They are different from Marjane's family because they are very rich, are used to a comfortable lifestyle, and the children are spoiled. 10. They overhear women making crude and bigoted comments about the women from southern Iran, simply because of diminishing resources due to the war. 11. Answers will vary.

The Key–The Passport: 1. Persians are so used to war that they simply accept the constant war around them and try to bear it. They are resigned to this kind of life from the many years of violence; Marjane's mother copes using this philosophy. 2. When music is played through the loudspeakers, the students must sing along and pound themselves on their chests; The students had seen many rituals where people hit themselves, whipped themselves, and even cut themselves. 3. They mock the rituals and disrespect the teachers' demands. The parents support their children and are very displeased with the teachers for forcing the students to follow the fundamentalist rules. 4. They say the keys will open the gates of heaven when the children die for the Iranian cause; The keys are really just pieces of plastic painted gold. 5. They have parties, serve alcohol, and dress and act in ways that are not approved by the government. Taji decides to hang heavy curtains on the windows to keep the neighbors from spying on them. 6. The soldiers accuse Eby of drinking, which is illegal, and they follow the family home to search the house. While Marjane and her grandmother go inside and pour the alcohol down the drains, Eby prevents a search of the house by bribing the police. 7. Iraq offers a settlement to the war and Saudi Arabia even offers to help rebuild, but Iran refuses this "imposed peace" and continues to fight. 8. She goes to the basement to think; She smokes a cigarette there, which she says makes her "a grown-up." 9. She sees people ordering others to give blood, wounded people lying on the floor, amputees, and patients suffering from chemical attacks; They are all victims of the war. 10. The man who was going to create a fake passport must leave Iran when the authorities hear of his activities, and Uncle Taher dies right before the real passport arrives. 11. Answers will vary.

Kim Wilde–The Dowry: 1. They go to Turkey. She asks for posters of Kim Wilde and Iron Maiden, a denim jacket, and chocolate. 2. They hide the posters in the lining of Eby's jacket. They bring Marjane the other requested items, Nike shoes, and a Michael Jackson pin. 3. A "Guardian of the Revolution" sees her wearing her scarf improperly and western-influenced attire; Marjane cries hysterically and says her cruel stepmother will punish and disown her if she gets in trouble. 4. Iraq uses new missiles called "Scuds" to attack Tehran. The Satrapis stay because Tehran is the best place in Iran for Marjane to continue her French education. 5. Scud missiles are bombing her neighborhood, so she runs home to see if her family is safe. She sees that the neighbor's house is destroyed, but her own house is still standing; She knows that her friend is dead when she sees her friend's turquoise bracelet in the rubble. 6. Marjane is wearing a bracelet, and her principal has warned her many times not to wear jewelry in class. When her principal tries to take away the bracelet, Marjane pusher her away, knocking her down. 7. Marjane's aunt knows people in the education system. Once Marjane starts the new school, her attitude gets her into trouble again when she tells the teachers that they are lying to the students. She is openly rebellious, where once she kept these sentiments hidden. 8. They want Marjane to continue to receive a good education, but they know that she will get into too much trouble in Iran and the government will try to silence her someday. They do not want to restrict their daughter's rebellious opinions because they agree with them, but they do not want her to die either. 9. She tells Marjane that she will meet "a lot of jerks" (p. 150), but Marjane must tell herself that they are stupid and not react with cruelty. 10. She sees that her mother has fainted and that her father is carrying her away. They both look despondent, and Marjane regrets turning back for one last look. 11. Answers will vary.

Note: Answers to Activities #8–#16 will vary. Suggested responses are given where applicable.

Activity #8: In the beginning: curious, hopeful; Event #1: Marjane must wear a veil—conflicted; Event #2: Marjane discovers that her grandfather was a prince—proud; Event #3: Marjane and Mehri are told they cannot demonstrate—determined; Event #4: Marjane listens to her Uncle Anoosh's stories—awe; Event #5: Marjane discovers that her Uncle Anoosh has been executed—despondent and later angry; Event #6: Marjane hears that her neighborhood is being bombed—terrified; At the end: rebellious, disenchanted

Activity #9: Victims: grandfather, Ahmadi, Mohsen, Siamak's sister, child soldiers, Neda, Niloufar; Victimizers: Reza, the Shah, fundamentalist government, Guardians of the Revolution; Fighters: grandfather, Uncle Fereydoon, Uncle Anoosh, Marjane; Peace-lovers: Mehri, Grandmother, Uncle Taher, Mrs. Nasrine; Conformists: Guardians of the Revolution, various principals and teachers; Self-directors: Marjane, Eby, Taji, grandfather, Uncle Fereydoon, Uncle Anoosh, Siamak, Mohsen; Possible theme based on self-directors: Independent thinking under a restrictive government can bring great hardship but also a sense of dignity, which makes the human spirit indomitable.

Activity #10: Line 1: Marjane; Line 2: family, freedom, bravery; Line 3: love, comfort, opinions; Line 4: hero, knowledge, relief; Line 5: westernized music, denim jacket, chocolate; Line 6: speaking her mind, reasoning, being stubborn; Line 7: her temper, impulsiveness, forgiveness; Line 8: Uncle Anoosh because of her openly rebellious behavior, her grandfather because of her strong stance against the class system, her mother because she defends women's rights; Line 9: bombings, tongue-lashings, emotional trauma; Line 10: Satrapi

Activity #11: Foreshadowing—As a young girl, Marjane wants to be "justice, love and the wrath of God all in one" (p. 9); Page—9; Clues—Marjane's sense of injustice in the world causes her to believe she is a prophet and write a "holy book" in which she explains how she would change the world; Coming Event—Marjane's sense of injustice compels her to be a rebel and an activist as she grows and matures; Foreshadowing— Eby notes the endless cycle of tyranny and submission over the last 2,500 years; Page—11; Clues—The current regime is the result of modern imperialism. In the picture, "our own emperors" and "Arab invasion" would follow modern imperialism. Coming Event—Iranians are oppressed by the government that results from their revolution and must defend themselves against the Iraqis; Foreshadowing—Marjane remarks that Marx looks a lot like God; Page—13; Clues—Marjane and God's talks become infrequent and less involved; Coming Event—Marjane loses interest in spiritual matters as she becomes preoccupied with politics; Foreshadowing—Mohsen is found drowned in the bathtub; Page—65; Clues—Anoosh twice insists that "Everything will be alright" (pp. 65, 66); Coming Event—Anoosh is arrested and executed; Foreshadowing—Uncle Taher comments that the stress of the war is bad for him; Page—118; Clues—Marjane mentions that Taher is prone to heart attacks; Coming Event— A grenade explodes near Taher's home, and he has a final heart attack and dies in the hospital; Foreshadowing— Marjane says that at 14 you do not need your parents anymore; Page—119; Clues—Taji says it scares her how blunt Marjane is, but Eby says that one day it will help her; Coming Event—Marjane leaves for Austria at the age of 14; Foreshadowing—Marjane comments that her mother is very permissive and that very few girls her age were allowed out alone; Page—131; Clues—Everyone on Gandhi Avenue seems very paranoid; Coming Event— Marjane is nearly arrested by the Guardians of the Revolution for her "improper" attire; Foreshadowing— Marjane says that in her parents' eyes, her future was linked to her French education; Page—137; Clues—Neda, who lives near Marjane, is killed and Marjane keeps getting in trouble at school; Coming Event—Marjane's parents decide she should go to Austria to continue her education.

Activity #12: Head: fiery ghosts in the theater; Heart: Eby leaving the airport with Taji in his arms; Funny bone: Marjane enjoying her posters; Feet: Neda's bracelet amidst the rubble

Activity #13: 1. Marjane sees Mehri eating in a separate room because of class restrictions. Effect: Marjane is compelled to be a force of justice in the world. 2. Marjane plans to exact revenge on Ramin for the people his father killed but is caught by Taji, who makes her consider how it would feel to be tortured. Effect: Marjane learns about forgiveness and channels her sense of injustice into nonviolent forms of expression. 3. Marjane meets Uncle Anoosh and listens to his views and stories. Effect: Marjane is inspired to be proactive in her beliefs. 4. Uncle Anoosh is executed. Effect: Marjane rejects God.

Activity #14: Answers will vary.

Activity #15: Book Title: *Persepolis*; Characters: Marjane, Eby, Taji, Grandmother, Mehri, Uncle Anoosh, Siamak, Mohsen, Mali, Uncle Taher; Setting: Tehran, Iran, 1978–1984; Conflicts: person vs. society, person vs. self, person vs. person; Possible Themes: coming of age, religion and politics, classism, war, death, love, loss, freedom; Point of View: first-person omniscient; Genre: memoir/graphic novel; Author's Style and Tone: black-and-white pictorial retrospective, anxious, suspicious, distraught, naïvely hopeful, overwhelmed, poignant, reflective, loving

Activity #16: Theme: secular world vs. religious fundamentalism; Symbol/Image: The first image on page 6; Relation: The image symbolizes the conflict between these two groups in society, as well as within Marjane in the beginning of the book; Theme: religion vs. politics, Symbol/Image: image of Marx and God on page 13; Relation: Marx and God are drawn similarly, symbolizing the shift in Marjane's interests, foreshadowing Marx's eventual replacement of God in her own mind, and the conflict between Communists and the religious zealots who rise to power; Theme: endless cycle of oppression; Symbol/Image: demon curled around panel where Eby talks of citizens' newfound freedom on page 43; Relation: The looming demon reinforces the idea that for Iranians, freedom is an illusion as long as the country has vast oil resources; Theme: coping with loss and its effect on one's spirituality; Symbol/Image: Marjane floating in space on page 71; Relation: Marjane feels isolated, totally dislocated from humanity and God, like some distant star; Theme: family solidarity amidst great adversity; Symbol/Image: the Satrapis on a flying carpet amidst European architecture on page 77; Relation: The image shows the Satrapis enjoying a brief respite from the stress of life in Iran, and the love that makes them so formidable in the face of adversity is clearly evident; Theme: theocratic oppression; Symbol/Image: Marjane and her classmates dressed identically and beating their chests on page 95; Relation: Marjane is indistinguishable from the other girls, all of whom look disturbed by the painful practice. The visual impact of the homogeneous self-injuring crowd is that religion is being used not to enrich individuals' lives, but to rob them of their dignity and independence; Theme: religion vs. politics and the ravages of war; Symbol/Image: child soldiers flailing in the air as they are blown up and Marjane and her friends flailing in the air, dancing on page 102; Relation: The author uses the juxtaposed images to express how the war (started by religious fundamentalists) has robbed children of their innocence.

Quiz #1: A. 1. F 2. T 3. T 4. T 5. F **B.** 6. martyr 7. doctor; prophet 8. revolution; bicycle (p. 10) 9. grandfather; water 10. The Shah (p. 27) **C.** Answers will vary. Refer to the scoring rubric on page 36 of this guide.

Quiz #2: A. 1. stories about children forced to work miserable jobs just to survive 2. He says, "…as long as there is oil in the Middle East we will never have peace" (p. 43). 3. A hero has spent time in jail in defense of his or her political ideals. 4. They both opposed the Shah's government and were considered political enemies of the state. Siamak is a Communist journalist, and Mohsen is a Communist revolutionary. 5. They treat each other like sisters. They are very close, comforting each other and playing and eating together. Marjane helps Mehri communicate with her boyfriend. **B.** 6. F 7. F 8. F 9. T 10. T **C.** Answers will vary. Refer to the scoring rubric on page 36 of this guide.

Quiz #3: A. 1. Marjane; star; spy (p. 69) 2. universities; decadent 3. fundamentalist 4. grandmother; Iraq 5. materialistic **B.** 6. b 7. d 8. e 9. c 10. a **C.** Answers will vary. Refer to the scoring rubric on page 36 of this guide.

Quiz #4: A. 1. They say it will open the gates of heaven when they die fighting for Iran; It is a plastic key painted gold. 2. to stop neighbors from spying on them and to keep debris from explosions from breaking their windows 3. It is where all the kids from the nice neighborhoods hang out, and it is where all the teenagers want to go to hang out with each other. 4. He needs to go outside the country for heart surgery. 5. He informs them that children are sent to army camps and trained to fight. They are made so eager to experience the afterlife that they are more than willing to die fighting for Iran. **B.** 6. F 7. T 8. F 9. F 10. T **C.** Answers will vary. Refer to the scoring rubric on page 36 of this guide.

Quiz #5: A. 1. F 2. T 3. F 4. T 5. F **B.** 6. posters; Turkey 7. Revolution; clothes 8. Austria (or Vienna) 9. dowry; government 10. exaggerate; skeptical **C.** Answers will vary. Refer to the scoring rubric on page 36 of this guide.

Final Test: A. 1. c 2. j 3. g 4. a 5. f 6. h 7. b 8. e 9. d 10. i **B.** 11. c 12. d 13. b 14. b 15. a 16. a 17. c 18. c 19. a 20. d 21. b **C.** 22. imperialists 23. fundamentalist; embassy (p. 72) 24. dowry 25. swans; bread 26. oil; peace (p. 43) 27. rebellious 28. Anoosh; God 29. prince; Communist **D.–E.** Answers will vary. Refer to the scoring rubric on page 36 of this guide.

Linking Novel Units® Student Packets to National and State Reading Assessments

During the past several years, an increasing number of students have faced some form of state-mandated competency testing in reading. Many states now administer state-developed assessments to measure the skills and knowledge emphasized in their particular reading curriculum. This Novel Units® guide includes open-ended comprehension questions that correlate with state-mandated reading assessments. The rubric below provides important information for evaluating responses to open-ended comprehension questions. Teachers may also use scoring rubrics provided for their own state's competency test.

Scoring Rubric for Open-Ended Items

3-Exemplary	Thorough, complete ideas/information Clear organization throughout Logical reasoning/conclusions Thorough understanding of reading task Accurate, complete response
2-Sufficient	Many relevant ideas/pieces of information Clear organization throughout most of response Minor problems in logical reasoning/conclusions General understanding of reading task Generally accurate and complete response
1-Partially Sufficient	Minimally relevant ideas/information Obvious gaps in organization Obvious problems in logical reasoning/conclusions Minimal understanding of reading task Inaccuracies/incomplete response
0-Insufficient	Irrelevant ideas/information No coherent organization Major problems in logical reasoning/conclusions Little or no understanding of reading task Generally inaccurate/incomplete response